by Edmund Harris
illustrated by Mary Teichman

SCHOOL PUBLISHERS

Printed in the United States of America

ISBN 10: 0-15-350513-3
ISBN 13: 978-0-15-350513-3

Ordering Options
ISBN 10: 0-15-350334-3 (Grade 4 Below-Level Collection)
ISBN 13: 978-0-15-350334-4 (Grade 4 Below-Level Collection)
ISBN 10: 0-15-357502-6 (package of 5)
ISBN 13: 978-0-15-357502-0 (package of 5)

1 2 3 4 5 6 7 8 9 10   179   12 11 10 09 08 07 06

We had been in the covered wagon for over five weeks, and my body was sore from being jostled so much. The Oregon Trail was bumpy, but it was the best way to get to the Oregon Territory. That's where my family and I were headed.

In the spring of 1841, my mother and father and I had loaded up our wagon and set out on the trail. We hoped to reach the Oregon Territory by late summer.

When we left Independence, Missouri, at the start of our journey, we were traveling with the Davis family. After just one week on the trail, the Davis family decided to turn back, but my father decided we would keep going.

For a while we traveled alone, although that's not the best way to do it. It's better to travel with other families, my father explained, because you could help one another out.

One day, we saw a wagon up ahead, and
when we pulled up to the wagon, we saw a
man and a boy looking at a snake on the ground.

"Look at that rattlesnake, Randy!" yelled
the man, smiling. When I saw that, I got scared
because even though they were safe in their
wagon, everyone knows you shouldn't go near
rattlesnakes.

"Uh, I think you should back away from the
snake, don't you, sir?" my father asked politely.
The man looked back at us. Then he stared
back at the snake, and a moment later it
slithered away.

They were the Smith family. Andrew and Elizabeth Smith were traveling with their five-year-old son, Randy, and six-month-old daughter, Betty. Mr. Smith, who was much younger than my father, steered the wagon. Mrs. Smith was very attentive to Betty.

When my father learned that the Smiths were also going to the Oregon Territory, he suggested that we all travel together. "Well, I like to do things my own way," Mr. Smith said. Eventually, though, he agreed, and our two families set off on the trail together.

After a few hours of traveling, we noticed a coyote off to the side of the trail. As we watched, the coyote darted forward and pounced on a chipmunk. When the coyote ran off, Mr. Smith yelled, "Wahoo!" and swerved his wagon to the right. He rode off in the direction of the coyote.

"Andrew, what are you doing?" my father called out, confused.

"I want to see that coyote!" Mr. Smith said. A few minutes later he got back on the trail. My father said that he thought Mr. Smith wasn't being very responsible.

Three days later, we came to the South Platte River, a large river that everyone traveling the Oregon Trail must cross. We got out of the wagons and looked at the river. It was wide and shallow but had many strong rapids. Rapids are water that moves very fast.

"It's not safe to cross here," my father said.

"Oh, come on, Dale. It's just fine here," replied Mr. Smith. "The water is shallow, so we can go right across." My father shook his head "no."

The men walked along the river. "The current is too strong, and there are too many rapids," my father said. "We should look for a safer place to cross."

"Where would that be?" asked Mr. Smith.

"We'll ride along the river until we find a place," my father replied.

"That could take us miles and miles out of our way! We could be out here for weeks! We'll *never* get to the Oregon Territory that way," Mr. Smith argued.

Mr. Smith walked back to his wagon and called to Randy. "Come on, Randy, we're going to cross right here," he said. He climbed onto the wagon and picked up the reins.

"Andrew, wait!" my father yelled. Mr. Smith turned to my father.

"Look, Dale, I want to be safe, but sometimes I have to take some risks," Mr. Smith said.

"You can't be both safe *and* risky—that's a contradiction," my father said. "Think of your family, Andrew."

Mr. Smith looked out at the river. He thought for a while and then seemed to come to his senses. "Dale, you're right. I don't think it's safe to cross here either. Let's go with your plan," he said.

My father smiled and said, "You made a good decision, Andrew." We then turned our wagons to the left and began to ride alongside the river. Just as Mr. Smith had said, it was slow and difficult. For days, we rode along the river, because it was still too dangerous to cross.

One day, we stopped for lunch along the river. I overheard the two men talking. "We need a new plan, Dale. We can't just ride forever. Maybe we should take a small risk and cross right here," Mr. Smith said to my father.

"No, Andrew, we just have to be patient. The most important thing is to keep our families safe," my father replied. Mr. Smith just looked away. He didn't want to lose more time, but he also realized that what my father said was true.

Later that day, we saw a large tree that had fallen across the river. The tree must have been blown down in a storm. The tree slowed the river water down, creating a safe place for us to cross.

"Here we go!" said Mr. Smith, seeing the slow, shallow water.

"Yes, sir!" my father yelled happily. We turned the wagons and crossed the river easily. Everyone was in a good mood as we rode back toward the Oregon Trail.

For six more weeks, we traveled with the Smiths toward the Oregon Territory. Mr. Smith seemed calmer than he had been when we first met him. He and my father solved many problems together.

One night, when we were all sitting around a campfire, Mr. Smith turned to me and said, "Your father is a wise man, and I've learned a lot from him. You won't see me chasing rattlesnakes or coyotes anymore." My father looked at Mr. Smith and smiled.

Think Critically

1. What is Mr. Smith like at the beginning of this story?

2. How do the two men resolve their disagreement about the river crossing?

3. Why does Mr. Smith dislike the idea of finding another place to cross the river?

4. What word means about the same thing as *pounced* does on page 7?

5. What did you learn from this story?

 Social Studies

Use a Map Use a map that shows the route of the Oregon Trail. Which states of the present day did the trail go through? Make a list of these states on a piece of paper.

 **School-Home Connection** Share this story with a family member. Then have a discussion about how people can learn from other people.